D0548352

Postman Pat
THE MOVIE
The Ultimate Storybook and More

igloobooks

igloobooks

Published in 2014
by Igloo Books Ltd
Cottage Farm
Sywell
NN6 0BJ
www.igloobooks.com

SHE001 0814
2 4 6 8 10 9 7 5 3 1
ISBN: 978-1-78343-892-1

Printed and manufactured in China

Postman Pat
THE MOVIE
The Ultimate Storybook and More

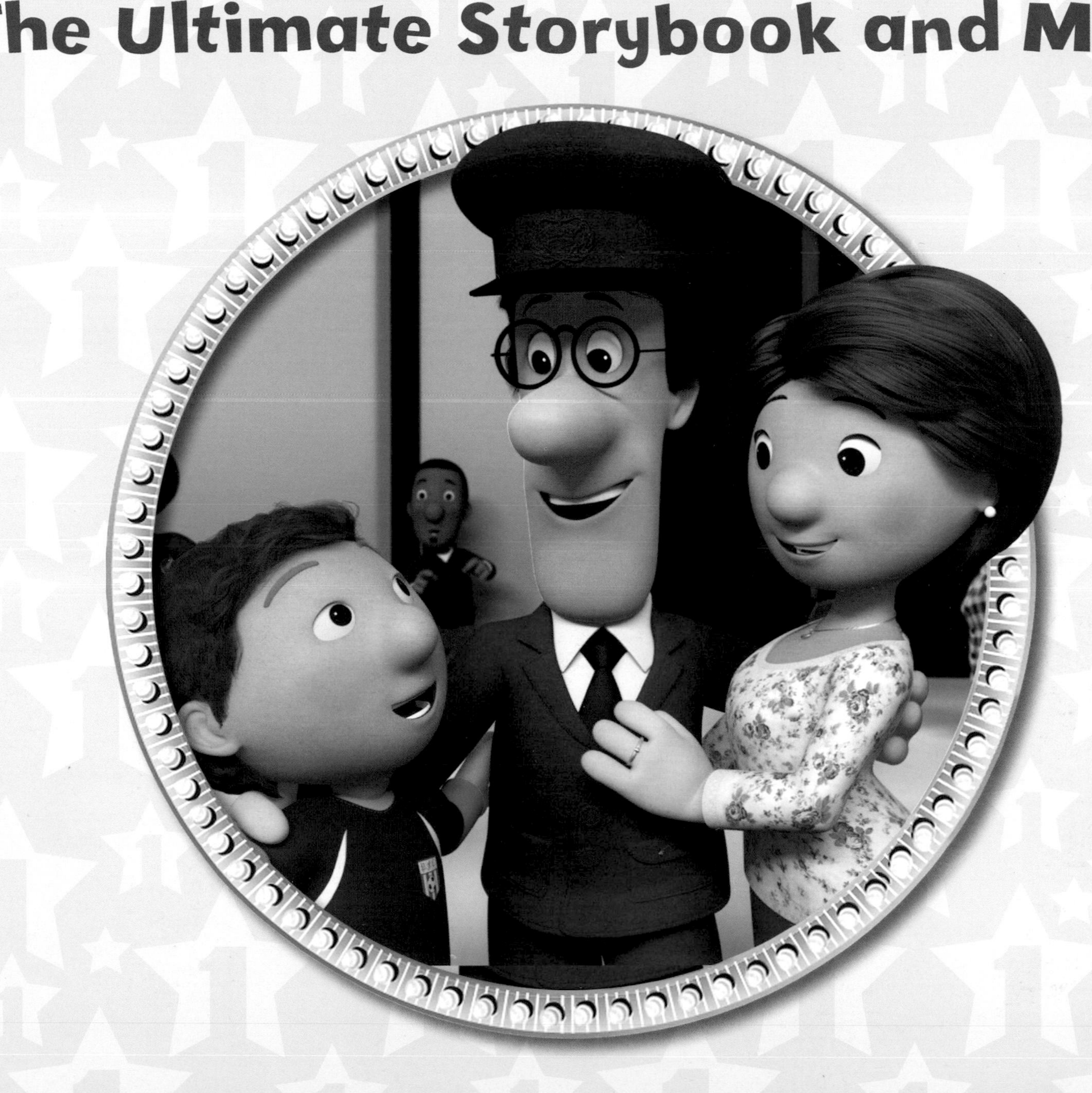

This igloo book belongs to:

Discover lots of fun facts about the characters you love most, as you read the story of Postman Pat: The Movie

It was a sunny morning in Greendale and Postman Pat was setting off for work.

"I get my bonus today," he told Sara and Julian.
"We can finally go on that dream holiday
to Italy."
"I can't wait!" said Sara, as Pat
waved goodbye.

When Pat got to work, there was a surprise waiting for him. Edwin Carbunkle, a new boss at the SDS, had brought in special machines for sorting the post, but they were causing chaos. Parcels were flying everywhere! Ben Taylor, Pat's manager, was trying to keep things under control, but it wasn't working.

At the end of the day, Carbunkle called the workers together. "Your deliveries are too slow," he said. "That means there's no bonus this year."
Pat was very sad. How could he tell Sara they couldn't go on their trip to Italy?

At home, Pat sat down beside Julian, who was watching a TV talent show.
"What's this?" asked Pat.
"It's called *You're the One!*" replied Julian. "It's brilliant!"

AM
FM

POSTMAN PAT

Postman Pat is a very happy man. He lives with his wife, Sara, their son Julian and their black and white cat called Jess. He has lived in Greendale village for most of his life and is friends with everyone who lives there, young and old. Pat loves his job as a postman. He'll always stop to lend someone a hand or have a friendly chat.

- Pat likes to start his day with a nice cup of tea and a round of toast.

- Pat is always on the go. To make deliveries to Greendale and Pencaster twice a day, Pat drives about 50 miles and walks roughly 10 miles.

- No delivery is too big or small. Pat has delivered everything from an industrial, sized magnet to a tiny, jewelled elephant.

Answers on page 96.

As Pat and Julian watched, the TV audience cheered loudly.
A wonderful singer called Josh had made it to the final.

"Next week, the auditions will take place in *Greendale*," announced Simon Cowbell, the judge of the show. "Remember, if *you* are the one, the first prize is a recording contract, as well as a dream holiday to Italy."
"Dad, did you hear that?" asked Julian. Pat had heard. He had an idea.

The morning after the audition, Pat was called to the SDS office. When he got there, Mr Brown and Carbunkle congratulated him on his success. They explained how they hoped to use Pat's fame to make the SDS more successful.

They wanted to make Postman Pat merchandise including, cakes, toys and dolls, all showing the SDS logo. As Pat became more famous, the SDS would be more famous, too! However, Carbunkle had a nastier plan.

"You'll be so busy with rehearsals, you won't have time for deliveries," whispered Carbunkle to Pat. "Let the Patbot 3000 do your work for you," he said, revealing the robot postman.

The Patbot looked like Pat, but with a strange smile. It repeated things like, "You can count on me," and, "The Special Delivery Service always gets through." Carbunkle convinced Pat that the robot would help him to win the competition and make the SDS more successful. Pat wasn't sure at all, but he agreed to keep the whole thing a secret.

CARBUNKLE

Edwin Carbunkle has been a techno-fan from an early age. He is fascinated with robots and computers. He has always believed that he can 'improve' the world, (and rule it himself) using technology. He does not believe in the 'human touch'. Now working for the Special Delivery Service (SDS), he is determined to impress the boss with his brilliant plans for robot delivery workers.

- Carbunkle uses his phone to control his gadgets. He can even find out about people just by pressing a few buttons.

- Carbunkle loves robots and has made dozens since he was a small boy. However, he finds it hard to make a robot that is liked by anyone other than him...

Answers on page 96.

Pat's first day of fame was a whirlwind. He appeared on a talk show with Josh, the other finalist and Josh's manager, Wilf. Everyone thought Pat was great, but Josh was bored and played computer games. His manager, Wilf, was so desperate to make everyone notice Josh that he talked too much and upset the show's presenter.

After the show, Wilf decided he must stop Postman Pat from winning, no matter what. "I am going to stamp out that postman," he snarled.

Meanwhile, back in Greendale, the Patbot was pretending to be Pat. He even had a Jessbot, too. No one knew that the real Pat had been replaced, but they did know that something wasn't quite as it should be.

The mail was all delivered on time, but Pat didn't stop to chat with Mrs Goggins, or wave at his friend Ted. Then, the Patbot almost ran over PC Selby! Had fame gone to Postman Pat's head? Had the villagers lost their friendly postman for good?

When the real Pat got back to the cottage that night, it was already late. "Pat, I'm worried about you," said Sara, sleepily. "Some of our friends called and said you had been acting strangely today."

The next day at the studio, Pat thought of the Patbot 3000 doing his rounds.
He hoped the robot was doing a good job and looking after his friends.
It was hard trying to keep the whole thing a secret while he became a celebrity.

SARA & JULIAN

Sara is married to Pat, whom she met when she worked for the Post Office. She's now a working mum and looks after her son, Julian, as well as running the Station Cafe with her friend Nisha Bains. She's a loving mum and wife and an active member of her village community.

- Sara once took over Pat's deliveries when he was ill.

- Sara runs the Station Cafe in Greendale.

- Julian is Pat and Sara's football-loving son. He is seven years old and goes to the local school. His best friends are Charlie and Meera. Julian dreams that when he grows up, he will be a professional footballer... or a postman, just like his dad!

Answers on page 96.

Pat became more and more famous, but he was beginning to change. One day, Sara noticed that Pat wasn't wearing his glasses. That made her feel very sad. She liked Pat's glasses and thought he didn't look right without them. "Remember to be home in time for tea with the Taylors and for Julian's football practice," said Sara, as Pat left.

Even Jess was starting to enjoy the attention.

With the cameras flashing, Jess decided to strike a pose.

Then another, and another.

No one noticed, because all the attention was on Pat.

Pat spent the day signing autographs and filming TV adverts. He was starting to love the attention and even began to forget about his post round and Greendale.

Sara waited with the Taylors for Pat to arrive, but he didn't come. She tried to call, but there was no answer. Pat even missed Julian's football match. Sara was starting to feel fed up of Pat being famous, but what could she do?

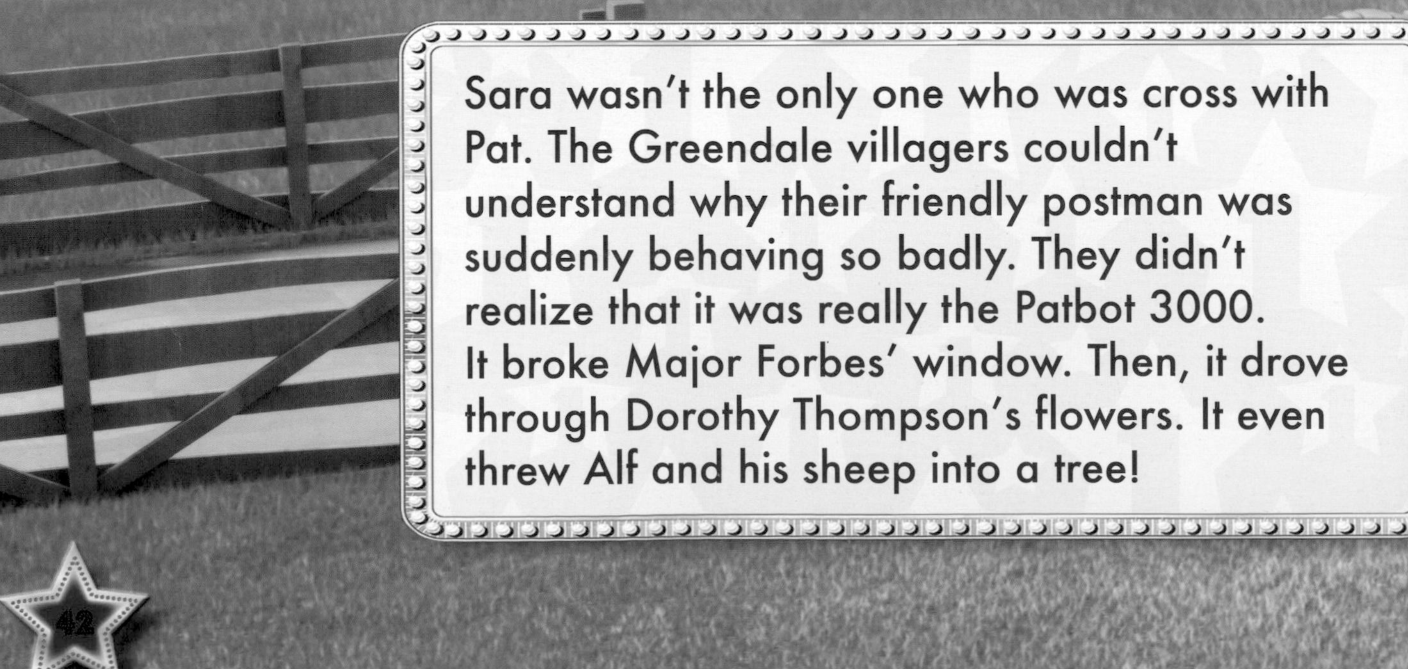

Sara wasn't the only one who was cross with Pat. The Greendale villagers couldn't understand why their friendly postman was suddenly behaving so badly. They didn't realize that it was really the Patbot 3000. It broke Major Forbes' window. Then, it drove through Dorothy Thompson's flowers. It even threw Alf and his sheep into a tree!

PATBOT

The Patbot 3000 is designed by Edwin Carbunkle to perfectly perform the tasks of a real-life postman. It makes all of its special deliveries perfectly on time. It does, however, still have a few teething problems, such as rudeness to customers, throwing parcels, breaking windows and generally causing chaos. Unfortunately, Carbunkle forgot to give his creation a 'human touch', so the Patbot 3000 definitely isn't a replacement for the real Postman Pat.

- Carbunkle based the Patbot 3000's big smile on that of Simon Cowbell himself!
- Patbot 3000's rubber skin is made from the same material used on the tyres of a jumbo jet.

Answers on page 96.

The villagers weren't the only ones who had been tricked by the Patbot.
Wilf was convinced that the Patbot 3000 was the real Pat as well!

He started to follow the Patbot, thinking it was Pat.

He put out road signs to make 'Pat' drive into a shark-infested river.

It didn't work. The Patbot just ignored them and crashed straight through.

Wilf started to think up a better plan to catch this pesky postman.

Wilf found a giant boulder to block the van.

It bounced across the hills and straight towards the van.

However, the strong Patbot picked up the heavy boulder. Wilf couldn't believe it!

The Patbot moved it out of the way and carried on with his round.

Finally, Wilf tried to stop the van with a tripwire.

The van came trundling down the road towards Wilf's cunning trap.

However, Patbot drove straight through it and the wire wrapped around Wilf instead.

Wilf was furious. He had to stop the postman from winning the show somehow.

One day, Sara went to see Pat in his rehearsal for the *You're the One!* final.

She told him how much she and Julian were missing him.

Pat was about to tell Sara everything about the trip to Italy and the Patbot 3000.

Then, suddenly, Carbunkle came along and sneakily sent Pat away.

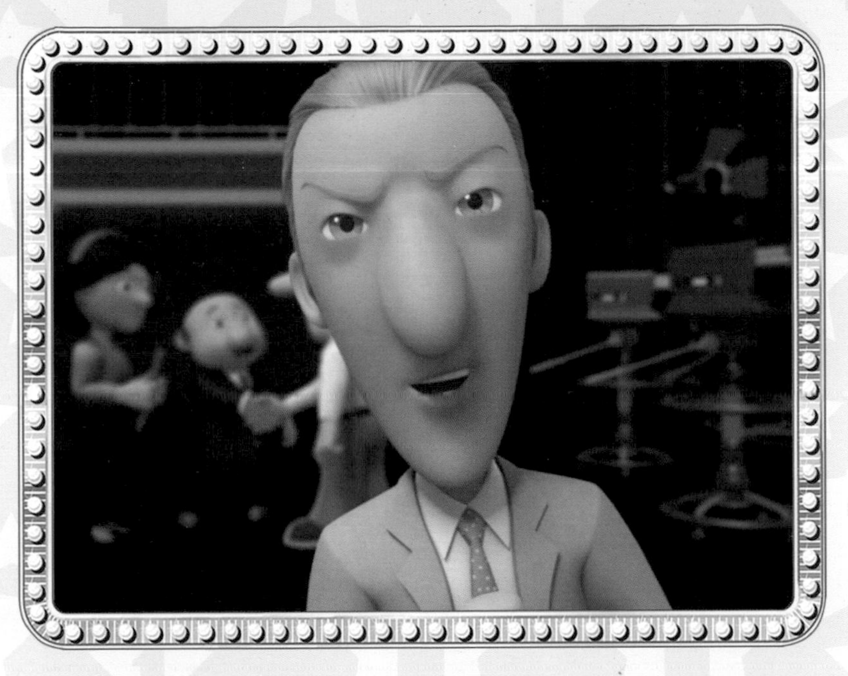

Carbunkle told Sara she was stopping Pat from becoming a big star.

"If you love someone, you have to let them go," he told her.

Jess heard Carbunkle and realised he was up to no good.

Before Jess could leave, Pat came back.

Heartbroken, Sara decided that if Pat really wanted fame, then she had better not get in his way. Meanwhile, Pat was speaking to Mr Brown, but when he hurried back to find Sara, she had left the studio. "She said she had other things to do," lied Carbunkle.

Then, when Pat wasn't looking, Carbunkle had Jess thrown out of the studios.

Now Pat had even lost his best friend. He was totally alone.

Julian was on his way home when he saw Jess walking alone.

Jess and Julian couldn't believe that Pat could let this happen.

Meanwhile, outside the SDS office, there was a crowd of angry people from Greendale. Everyone had come to complain about one thing – Postman Pat!

SUFFICIENT
POSTAGE
Father Christmas
North Pol
RETURN
TO SENDER

MR BROWN

When Mr Brown was younger, he dreamed of being a postman. He used to dress up in a cap and carry a pretend postbag everywhere he went. When at last he grew up, Mr Brown decided it wasn't just post that he wanted to deliver, but special deliveries. After years of hard work, he now owns the Special Delivery Service and makes parcels go anywhere, to anyone, whatever it takes!

Mr Brown owns the first ever post van that was driven in Greendale. He polishes it every weekend and still takes it out for a spin.

BEN TAYLOR

Ben Taylor got his first job working as a delivery boy for the SDS. Since then, he has climbed the ranks to reach the job of manager, owing to his enthusiasm and hard work. He believes that helping other people is the most important work a person can do.

Ben is Postman Pat's manager at the SDS.

Ben is married to Lauren – the teacher at the local school.

At the SDS, Ben was trying to calm the angry crowd down.

"Pat's been under a lot of pressure lately," he said.

Just then, Carbunkle appeared from inside with the Patbot 3000.

"Taylor," he said to Ben, "you're fired. I'm replacing you with Pat."

Ben was shocked. He couldn't believe his friend, Pat, would do this to him.
The crowd all gasped.

Carbunkle wasn't finished. He fired all of the other SDS employees, too! Carbunkle was ready for the final stage of his plan. He was replacing all the delivery workers with super-efficient robots.

The villagers were shocked and started to leave.

"I can't believe Pat would do this to us," said one worker.

Julian was shocked, too. "Aren't the most important things in the world friends and family, Dad?" he asked.

"The most important things are efficiency, profit and success," replied the Patbot.

As everyone left, the doors on the post vans opened up and out marched dozens of Patbots. They all chanted, "Efficiency, profit, success," together.

"Now that everyone hates Postman Pat, they won't mind if I replace every delivery man with my glorious, money-making machines," chuckled Carbunkle, wickedly.

"I will be the boss of SDS and
I won't stop there," he continued.
"Today England! Tomorrow,
the world!" At that moment,
the army of Patbot 3000s took
to the skies and flew away to
do Carbunkle's evil work.

PENCASTER
SORTING OFFICE
PAT 4
PAT 4

JESS

Pat's right-hand-cat for many years, Jess has a way of 'talking' with the simplest of meows and a twitch of his whiskers. He has helped Pat through many scrapes and is an essential part of Pat's working day, making sure that deliveries reach their destinations on time and in one piece. When not working, Jess likes to eat fish, drink milk and watch other cats chasing mice.

- For supper, Jess likes to eat fish.
- Jess likes to chase mice, although he has never caught one.

Answers on page 96.

At last, it was the final night of *You're the One!*

"Sara, Julian, it's time to go," said Pat.

Sara and Julian told him they weren't coming. Jess didn't want to go either.

It seemed that no one from Greendale wanted to support Pat.

Meanwhile, in Greendale, Ben was out for a walk.

He saw Pat in a post van. Then he saw another! "Two Pats?" thought Ben.

Ben had to know what was going on with his friend Pat.

Ben found Jess and together they raced after one of the vans, towards the SDS.

At the SDS, Ben and Jess watched the Patbot and the Jessbot go inside.

Meanwhile, inside, Wilf was waiting for Pat, too.

Wilf had set up a trap that he was sure would stop the pesky postman.

He dropped a huge crate, which crashed down on the Patbot.

Wilf excitedly went to check that he'd captured Pat.

Suddenly, there was a strange noise and out burst the Patbot!

"Efficiency, profit, success!" it cried, marching towards Wilf.

The Patbot marched towards Wilf and the Jessbot's eyes glowed a bright red.

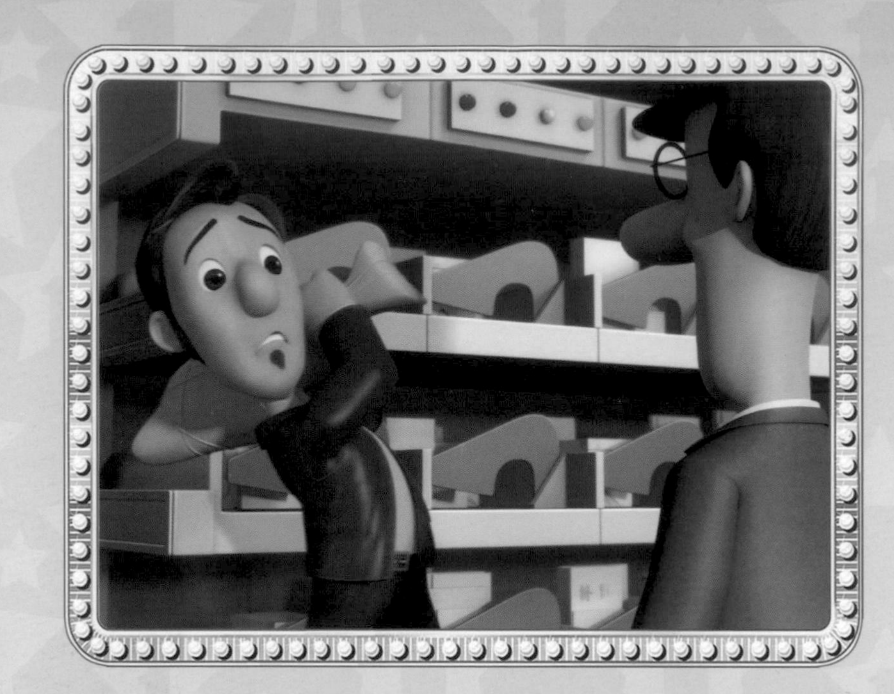

Wilf backed away and picked up a giant, fish-shaped package to hit the Patbot with.

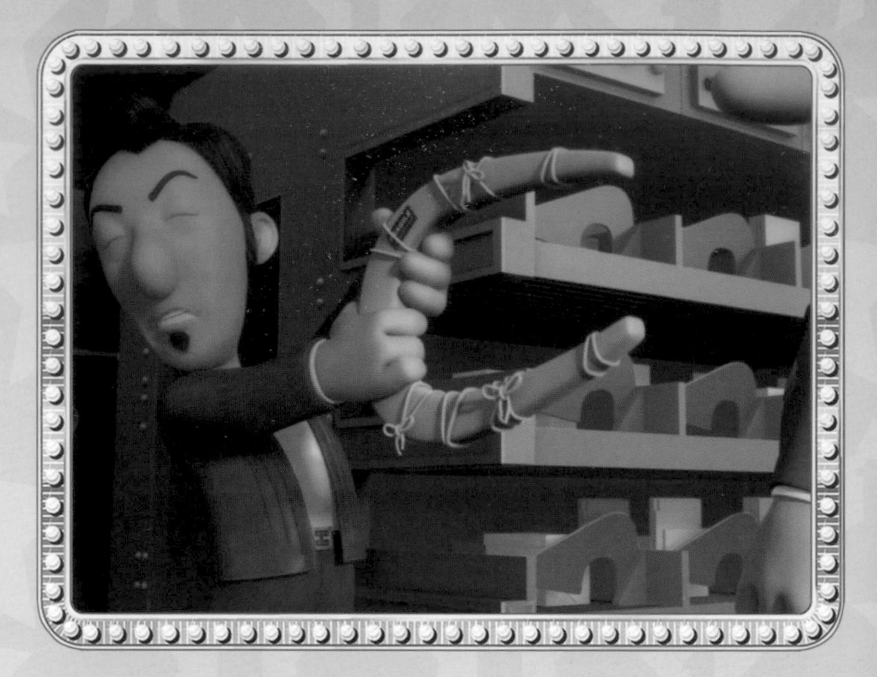

Then, he grabbed a horseshoe-shaped package instead.

It was a magnet! Wilf pointed the package at the Patbot and it began to shake.

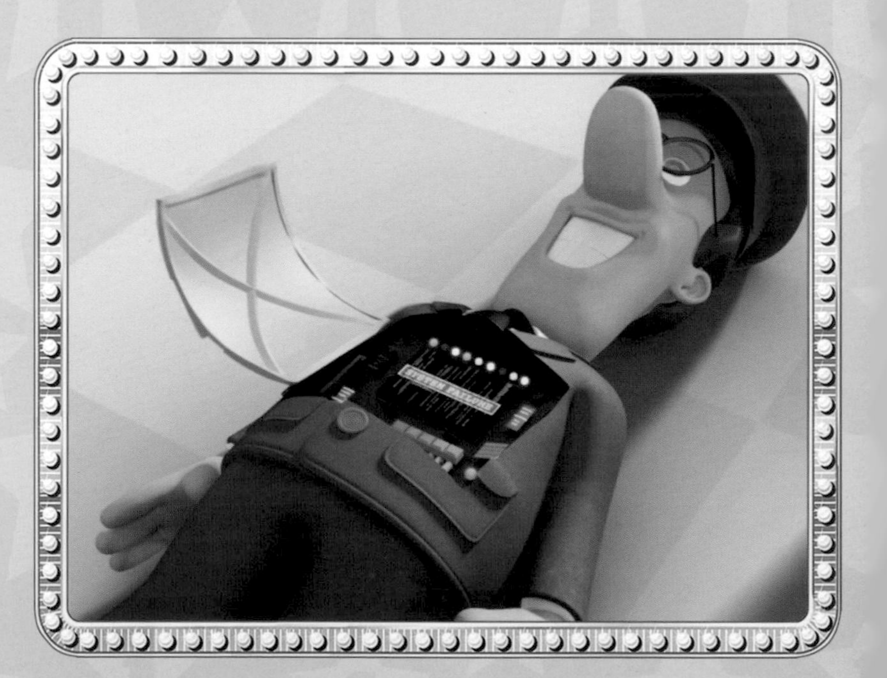

When the Patbot collapsed, Wilf saw the flashing lights and buttons inside. "He's a robot!" he cried.

Sara called everyone together in Greendale Village Hall.

"Pat's always been there for us and now we need to be there for him," she said.

Everyone agreed. Sara, Julian, Jess and the villagers immediately got in the car and roared down the road to the station.

Everyone jumped onto the Greendale Rocket and set off for London to support Pat.

JOSH

Josh is a great singer, and a smash hit on *You're the One!* but his main interest is computer games. Josh has been trained by Wilf, his manager, so that he is certain to win *You're the One!* and become a big star.

Josh likes singing, but unlike his manager, he believes in fair play and letting the best person win. After all, the only thing anyone can do is try their best. When the competition is over, he hopes to go back to playing his computer games...

Josh is a good singer and an ace at computer games!

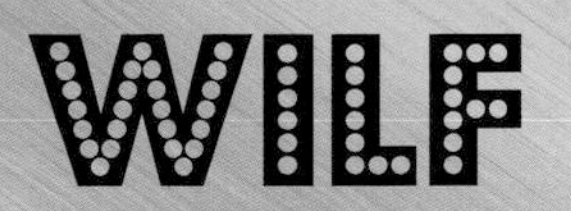

WILF

From an early age, Wilf has wanted to make it big. As a child, he entered all the talent competitions, singing his heart out, but he never won. His years of touring had shown him that behind every successful singer was a good manager. He may not be the one in the spotlight, but he can still live the luxury lifestyle he has dreamed of by helping Josh achieve stardom.

- After years of failure, Wilf had to admit that he wasn't talented enough to be a singer.
- Wilf was born in Scotland.
- Wilf is terribly allergic to cats.

In London, the show was about to start. Pat didn't want to go on without his friends and family to support him. "I'm not a performer. I'm a postman," he told Carbunkle, but Carbunkle just laughed and brought out a Patbot. "Sorry Pat, I don't need you anymore," he said.

The Patbot 3000 was even going to take Pat's place on the show! Carbunkle locked Pat in the dressing room and headed to the stage with the Patbot.

Suddenly, Pat heard a noise from the window. Jess had come to rescue him!

They climbed out of the window and landed in the street outside. Before they could move, they were surrounded by an army of Patbots. They tried to escape up a ladder, but the Jessbot came after them and chased them onto the roof. The Jessbot shot at them with its deadly laser eyes, but the laser bounced off Pat's hat badge and hit the Jessbot instead!

Quickly, Pat and Jess found a way down from the roof, just above the main stage of the studio. The final of *You're the One!* had already started. Below them, the Patbot 3000 was singing Pat's song!

Suddenly, Wilf burst onto the stage. "That's not a real singer – it's a robot!" he cried. Wilf broke the Patbot with a magnet to show everyone. The audience gasped with surprise. "Robots are not allowed on the show," said Simon Cowbell.

JESSBOT

With his red glowing eyes and scary meow, the Jessbot is definitely not the friendliest feline. Created by Carbunkle as the perfect companion for the Patbot 3000, the Jessbot offers his own kind of support in tricky situations. He has a deep, loud growl to scare off troublesome postmen and his eyes can work as laser beams that cut through steel or anything else that gets in the way!

- Jessbot has a larger computer chip than the Patbot 3000, because being a postman's companion is a far trickier job than just delivering post.
- Jessbot's lasers can shoot beams up to 1 mile away!

Answers on page 96.

At that moment, Pat dropped down onto the stage. "Wait! I can explain everything," he said. "I got into this contest to win a holiday for my wife, but I forgot to take time for those I really care about."

Everyone felt sorry for Pat, except for Carbunkle. With his phone, he brought his Patbot army to the studio. "The future belongs to me and to machines!" he laughed. Suddenly, the whole studio was full of Patbot 3000s!

As everyone panicked and rushed around, Josh calmly picked up Carbunkle's phone. He started to press a few buttons. Suddenly, the Patbots all stopped.
"Easiest game ever," said Josh.

Carbunkle tried to pretend that the robots were all Mr Brown's idea.

"I'm sorry, Pat," said Mr Brown. "I had no idea what was going on!"

"This is not the SDS way," he said and fired Carbunkle.

Carbunkle and his robots were taken away. "You can't do this!" he cried.

Pat thought he stood no chance of winning the contest anymore. As he turned to go, he suddenly saw some friendly faces in the crowd. Sara, Julian and all of Greendale had come after all.

So, Pat took to the stage and sang. Simon announced that Pat was the winner and he won the holiday for Sara. Pat was pleased but best of all, he realised that he had always been a star to his own family and friends.

For his deliveries, Pat also uses a motorbike and a snowmobile.

Pat's Post Van

Pat's van, the most important vehicle in Greendale's postal delivery service, comes complete with a wave from its driver and sometimes a friendly 'beep'. It is a familiar and welcome sight around the village of Greendale. Pat's red van sets off just as day is dawning, delivering far and wide, until all letters and parcels have reached their destination.

The Greendale Rocket
Greendale's train carries passengers from the village and also plays a vital role in getting the mail to other towns. Driven by Pat's friend Ajay, the train and station are an important part of life in Greendale.

SDS Helicopter
For really tricky jobs, the SDS has a helicopter which Pat can fly. The helicopter can get the job done super fast and in super style. Sometimes it's even called on to make special deliveries that are not really part of a normal postman's job.

CAN YOU SPOT THE CLOSE-UPS?

Now that you have read the fantastic story of Postman Pat: The Movie, why not look back through the book and see if you can find all of these close-up images? Once you think you've found them all, check the answer page to see if you were right.

1. Sara's newspaper
2. Ben with boxes
3. Pat's radio
4. Simon's mug
5. Pat's boom box
6. Mr Brown and toys

JESSBOT IN THE VAN

JESS'S PHOTO

PAT SIGNING AUTOGRAPHS

JESS'S PAW PRINTS

UPSIDE DOWN SHEEP

BEN AND LIZZY

SARA ON THE TRAIN

PAT'S MIRROR

CORNERED BY PATBOTS

ANSWERS

Did you get all the questions right? Check the answers below to find out.

PAGE 13

Q: What is the name of Pat's Manager at the SDS?

A: **Ben Taylor.**

PAGE 21

Q: What was the name of the singer who made it to the talent show final?

A: **Josh.**

PAGE 29

Q: How did Carbunkle try to convince Postman Pat to be replaced by the Patbot 3000?

A: **He told him he would be too busy with rehearsals to make his own deliveries.**

PAGE 37

Q: Why did Sara think Pat had changed?

A: **He didn't stop to chat to Mrs Goggins, or wave at Ted.**

PAGE 45

Q: Can you list three things the Patbot 3000 did wrong during its deliveries?

A: **It broke Major Forbes' window, it drove through Dorothy Thompson's flowers and it threw Alf and his sheep into a tree.**

PAGE 69

Q: What does Jess want to tell Pat when he's thrown out of the studio?

A: **That he heard Carbunkle telling Sara she was stopping Pat from becoming a big star.**

PAGE 86

Q: How did Pat and Jess escape the Jessbot's laser beam up on the roof?

A: **The laser bounced off the badge on Pat's hat and hit the Jessbot.**

PAGES 94 - 95

1. Page 7 **2.** Page 9 **3.** Page 11 **4.** Page 15 **5.** Page 17 **6.** Page 26 **7.** Page 33 **8.** Page 34 **9.** Page 40 **10.** Page 41 **11.** Page 43 **12.** Page 61 **13.** Page 75 **14.** Page 78 **15.** Page 87